KU-676-982

ANIMAL FAIR

American Folksong

Copyright © 1999 by HAL LEONARD CORPORATION
International Copyright Secured   All Rights Reserved

PIANO • VOCAL • GUITAR

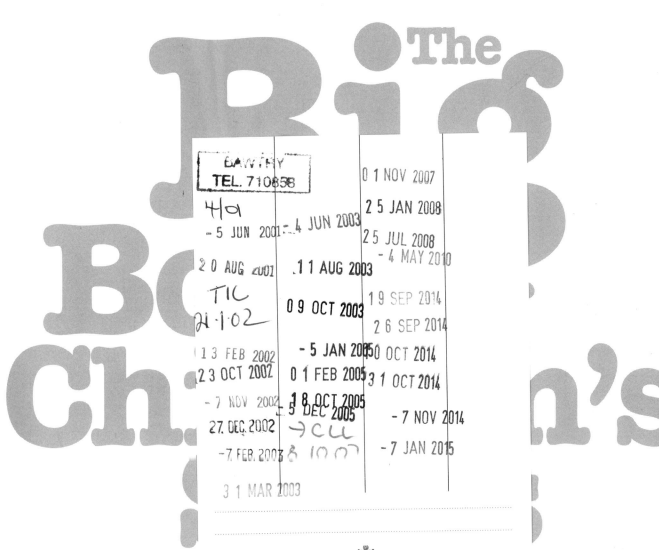

BAWTRY
TEL. 710858

4/a

-5 JUN 2001 -4 JUN 2003   0 1 NOV 2007
                            2 5 JAN 2008
2 0 AUG 2001 .1 1 AUG 2003 2 5 JUL 2008
                             - 4 MAY 2010
TIC
21·1·02   0 9 OCT 2003   1 9 SEP 2014
                             2 6 SEP 2014
1 3 FEB 2002 - 5 JAN 2005   0 OCT 2014
2 3 OCT 2002 0 1 FEB 2005   3 1 OCT 2014
- 7 NOV 2002 1 8 OCT 2005
27. DEC. 2002 3 DEC 2005   - 7 NOV 2014
              ⟶CU
-7 FEB 2003   - 7 JAN 2015

3 1 MAR 2003

DONCASTER
Doncaster Metropolitan Borough Council

DONCASTER LIBRARY AND INFORMATION SERVICES

Please return/renew this item by the last date shown.
Thank you for using your library.

WH2594 server

DONCASTER LIBRARY SERVICE

30122 01795394 0

This publication is not authorised for sale in the
United States of America and/or Canada.

HLE

Hal Leonard Europe
Distributed by Music Sales

Exclusive Distributors:
Music Sales Limited
8/9 Frith Street, London W1D 3JB, England.
Music Sales Pty Limited
120 Rothschild Avenue, Rosebery, NSW 2018, Australia.

Order No. HLE90000990
ISBN 0-7119-8271-6
This book © Copyright 2000 by Hal Leonard Europe

Unauthorised reproduction of any part of this publication
by any means including photocopying is an infringement
of copyright.

Printed in the USA

Your Guarantee of Quality
As publishers, we strive to produce every book to the highest
commercial standards.
The book has been carefully designed to minimise awkward
page turns and to make playing from it a real pleasure.
Throughout, the printing and binding have been planned
to ensure a sturdy, attractive publication which should give
years of enjoyment.
If your copy fails to meet our high standards, please inform
us and we will gladly replace it.

Music Sales' complete catalogue describes thousands of titles
and is available in full colour sections by subject, direct from
Music Sales Limited. Please state your areas of interest and
send a cheque/postal order for £1.50 for postage to:
Music Sales Limited, Newmarket Road, Bury St. Edmunds,
Suffolk IP33 3YB, England.

· www.musicsales.com

DONCASTER LIBRARY AND
INFORMATION SERVICE

017953940

Music
Exchange 04/01

780.21 £19   No price

ANY DREAM WILL DO

from JOSEPH AND THE AMAZING TECHNICOLOR® DREAMCOAT

Music by ANDREW LLOYD WEBBER
Lyrics by TIM RICE

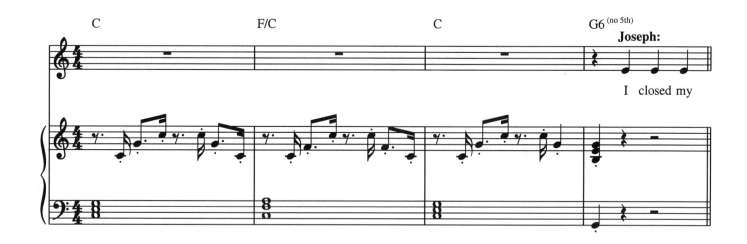

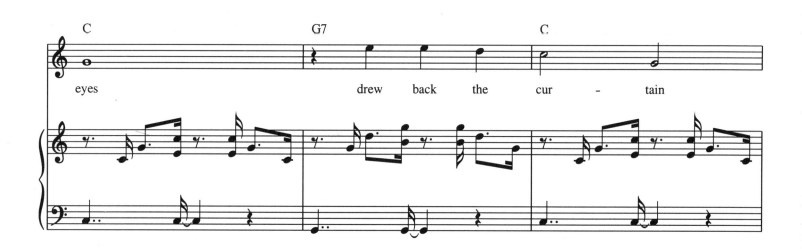

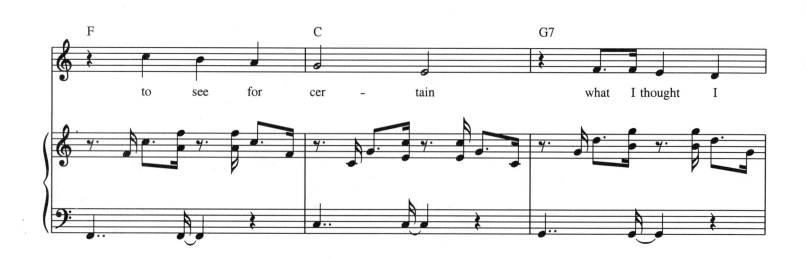

© Copyright 1969 The Really Useful Group Ltd.
Copyright Renewed
All Rights for North America Controlled by Williamson Music Co.
International Copyright Secured   All Rights Reserved

BAA BAA BLACK SHEEP

Traditional

Copyright © 1999 by HAL LEONARD CORPORATION
International Copyright Secured   All Rights Reserved

THE BARE NECESSITIES

from Walt Disney's THE JUNGLE BOOK

Words and Music by
TERRY GILKYSON

Look for the bare ne - ces - si - ties, the

sim - ple bare ne - ces - si - ties; ___ for - get a - bout your

wor - ries and your strife.

I mean the
I mean the
I mean the

© 1964 Wonderland Music Company, Inc.
Copyright Renewed
All Rights Reserved   Used by Permission

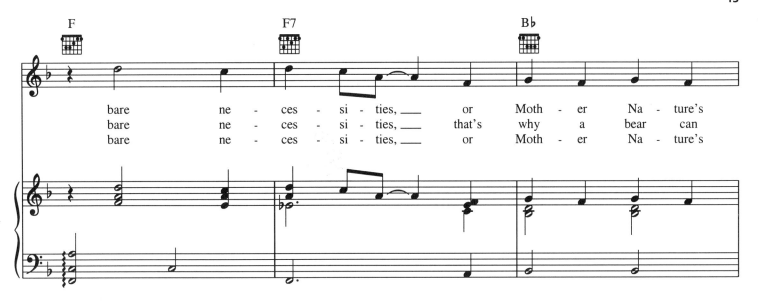

bare ne - ces - si - ties, ___ or Moth - er Na - ture's
bare ne - ces - si - ties, ___ that's why a bear can
bare ne - ces - si - ties, ___ or Moth - er Na - ture's

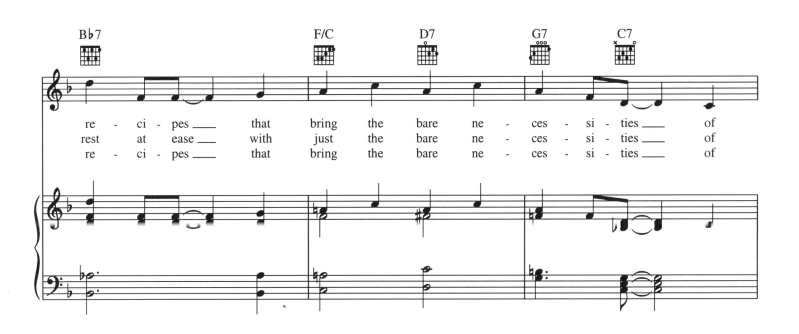

re - ci - pes ___ that bring the bare ne - ces - si - ties ___ of
rest at ease ___ with just the bare ne - ces - si - ties ___ of
re - ci - pes ___ that just bring the bare ne - ces - si - ties ___ of

life. _____ Wher - ev - er I wan - der, _____
life. _____ When you ___ pick a paw - paw _____
life. _____ So just try to re - lax Spoken: Oh Yeah!

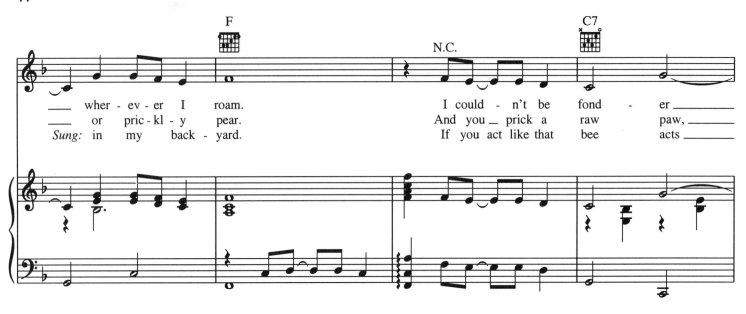

_____ wher - ev - er I roam.
_____ or pric - kl - y pear.
Sung: in my back - yard.

I could - n't be fond - er _____
And you_ prick a raw paw, _____
If you act like that bee acts _____

_____ of my big home.
_____ next time be - ware.
_____ you're work - in' too hard.

The bees are buzz - in' in the
Don't pick the prick - ly pear by
Don't spend your time just look - in' a -

tree to make some hon - ey just for me.
paw, when you pick a pear, try to use the claw.
round for some - thing you want that can't be found.

But
When

BE OUR GUEST
from Walt Disney's BEAUTY AND THE BEAST

Lyrics by HOWARD ASHMAN
Music by ALAN MENKEN

Moderately

Lumiere: Ma chere Mademoiselle,

it is with deepest pride and greatest pleasure that we welcome you

tonight. And now, we invite you to relax. Let us pull up a chair as the

poco rit.

© 1991 Walt Disney Music Company and Wonderland Music Company, Inc.
All Rights Reserved   Used by Permission

Slower, melancholy

guest! Be our guest!

Lumiere: Life is so un-

nerv - ing for a ser - vant who's not serv - ing. He's not

whole with - out a soul to wait up - on. _____

Ah, those good old days when we were use - ful.

BEAUTY AND THE BEAST

from Walt Disney's BEAUTY AND THE BEAST

Lyrics by HOWARD ASHMAN
Music by ALAN MENKEN

© 1991 Walt Disney Music Company and Wonderland Music Company, Inc.
All Rights Reserved   Used by Permission

33

BELLA NOTTE
(This Is the Night)
from Walt Disney's LADY AND THE TRAMP

Words and Music by PEGGY LEE
and SONNY BURKE

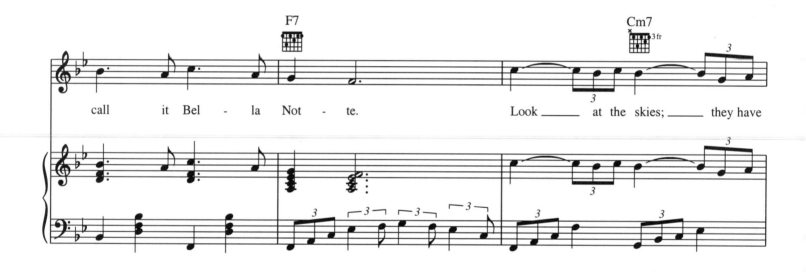

© 1952 Walt Disney Music Company
Copyright Renewed
All Rights Reserved   Used by Permission

BIBBIDI-BOBBIDI-BOO
(The Magic Song)
from Walt Disney's CINDERELLA

Words by JERRY LIVINGSTON
Music by MACK DAVID and AL HOFFMAN

Sa - la - ga - doo - la men - chic - ka boo - la bib - bi - di - bob - bi - di - boo Put 'em to - geth - er and what have you got bib - bi - di - bob - bi - di - boo. Sa - la - ga - doo - la men - chic - ka boo - la bib - bi - di - bob - bi - di - boo. It - 'll do mag - ic be - lieve it or not,

© 1948 Walt Disney Music Company
Copyright Renewed
All Rights Reserved   Used by Permission

A BICYCLE BUILT FOR TWO
(Daisy Bell)

Words and Music by
HARRY DACRE

Copyright © 1991 by HAL LEONARD CORPORATION
International Copyright Secured   All Rights Reserved

A DREAM IS A WISH YOUR HEART MAKES

from Walt Disney's CINDERELLA

Words and Music by MACK DAVID,
AL HOFFMAN and JERRY LIVINGSTON

© 1948 Walt Disney Music Company
Copyright Renewed
All Rights Reserved   Used by Permission

THE BLUE TAIL FLY
(Jimmy Crack Corn)

Words and Music by
DANIEL DECATUR EMMETT

Copyright © 2000 by HAL LEONARD CORPORATION
International Copyright Secured   All Rights Reserved

CAMPTOWN RACES

Copyright © 1988 by HAL LEONARD PUBLISHING CORPORATION
International Copyright Secured   ALL RIGHTS RESERVED   Printed in the U.S.A.

CHIM CHIM CHER-EE
from Walt Disney's MARY POPPINS

Words and Music by RICHARD M. SHERMAN
and ROBERT B. SHERMAN

© 1963 Wonderland Music Company, Inc.
Copyright Renewed
International Copyright Secured All Rights Reserved

Tempo 1

CLEMENTINE

Copyright © 1988 by HAL LEONARD PUBLISHING CORPORATION
International Copyright Secured   ALL RIGHTS RESERVED   Printed in the U.S.A.

CRUELLA DE VIL

from Walt Disney's 101 DALMATIANS

Words and Music by
MEL LEVEN

© 1959 Walt Disney Music Company
Copyright Renewed
International Copyright Secured   All Rights Reserved

DO-RE-MI
from THE SOUND OF MUSIC

Lyrics by OSCAR HAMMERSTEIN II
Music by RICHARD RODGERS

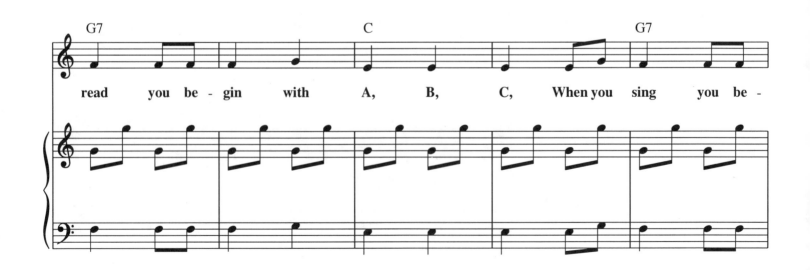

Copyright © 1959 by Richard Rodgers and Oscar Hammerstein II
Copyright Renewed
WILLIAMSON MUSIC owner of publication and allied rights throughout the world
International Copyright Secured   All Rights Reserved

EENSY WEENSY SPIDER

Traditional

The een-sy ween-sy spi-der went up the wa-ter spout; Down came the rain and washed the spi-der out. Out came the sun and dried up all the rain; Now the een-sy ween-sy spi-der went up the spout a-gain.

Copyright © 2000 by HAL LEONARD CORPORATION
International Copyright Secured   All Rights Reserved

EV'RYBODY WANTS TO BE A CAT
from Walt Disney's THE ARISTOCATS

Words by FLOYD HUDDLESTON
Music by AL RINKER

© 1968 Walt Disney Music Company
Copyright Renewed
All Rights Reserved   Used by Permission

'cause ev - 'ry - thing else is ob - so - lete.   A

square with a horn ___ makes you wish you weren't born ___ ev - 'ry

time he plays! ___   But with a

square in the act, ___ you can set mu - sic back ___ to the

FEED THE BIRDS
from Walt Disney's MARY POPPINS

Words and Music by RICHARD M. SHERMAN
and ROBERT B. SHERMAN

© 1963 Wonderland Music Company, Inc.
Copyright Renewed
International Copyright Secured   All Rights Reserved

Tempo I

Though _____ her words are sim - ple _____ and few,

lis - ten, _____ lis - ten, _____ she's call - ing to you:

"Feed _____ the birds, tup - pence _____ a bag,

tup - pence, _____ tup - pence, _____ tup - pence _____ a bag."

FRÈRE JACQUES

Copyright © 1988 by HAL LEONARD PUBLISHING CORPORATION
International Copyright Secured   ALL RIGHTS RESERVED   Printed in the U.S.A.

FRIEND LIKE ME
from Walt Disney's ALADDIN

Lyrics by HOWARD ASHMAN
Music by ALAN MENKEN

© 1992 Walt Disney Music Company and Wonderland Music Company, Inc.
All Rights Reserved   Used by Permission

FROG WENT A-COURTIN'

Anonymous

Copyright © 1995 by HAL LEONARD CORPORATION
International Copyright Secured   All Rights Reserved

sword and pis - tol by his side, uh -

huh, uh - huh. (2. - 15.) huh.

Additional Lyrics

2. Well, he rode down to Miss Mouses's door, uh-huh, uh-huh.
   Well, he rode down to Miss Mouses's door,
   Where he had often been before, uh-huh, uh-huh.

3. He took Miss Mousie on his knee, uh-huh, uh-huh.
   He took Miss Mousie on his knee,
   Said, "Miss Mousie will you marry me?" Uh-huh, uh-huh.

4. "I'll have to ask my Uncle Rat, etc.
   See what he will say to that." etc.

5. "Without my Uncle Rat's consent,
   I would not marry the President."

6. Well, Uncle Rat laughed and shook his fat sides,
   To think his niece would be a bride.

7. Well, Uncle Rat rode off to town
   To buy his niece a wedding gown.

8. "Where will the wedding supper be?"
   "Way down yonder in a hollow tree."

9. "What will wedding supper be?"
   "A fried mosquito and a roasted flea."

10. First to come in were two little ants,
    Fixing around to have a dance.

11. Next to come in was a bumble bee,
    Bouncing a fiddle on his knee.

12. Next to come in was a fat sassy lad,
    Thinks himself as big as his dad.

13. Thinks himself a man indeed,
    Because he chews the tobacco weed.

14. And next to come in was a big tomcat,
    He swallowed the frog and the mouse and the rat.

15. Next to come in was a big old snake,
    He chased the party into the lake.

GETTING TO KNOW YOU

from THE KING AND I

Lyrics by OSCAR HAMMERSTEIN II
Music by RICHARD RODGERS

It's a ver-y an-cient say-ing But a true and hon-est thought, That if you be-come a teach-er, by your pu-pils you'll be taught. As a teach-er, I've been

Copyright © 1951 by Richard Rodgers and Oscar Hammerstein II
Copyright Renewed
WILLIAMSON MUSIC owner of publication and allied rights throughout the world
International Copyright Secured   All Rights Reserved

GOOSEY, GOOSEY GANDER

Traditional

Copyright © 2000 by HAL LEONARD CORPORATION
International Copyright Secured   All Rights Reserved

HAKUNA MATATA

from Walt Disney Pictures' THE LION KING

Music by ELTON JOHN
Lyrics by TIM RICE

© 1994 Wonderland Music Company, Inc.
All Rights Reserved Used by Permission

cer - tain ap - peal. ___ He could clear the sa - van - nah af - ter ev - 'ry meal! ___ *Pumbaa:* I'm a

sen - si - tive soul, though I seem thick - skinned. And it

hurt that my friends nev - er stood down - wind!

And, oh, ___ the shame! *Timon:* He was a - shamed! *Pumbaa:* Thought of chang - in' my

HEY DIDDLE DIDDLE

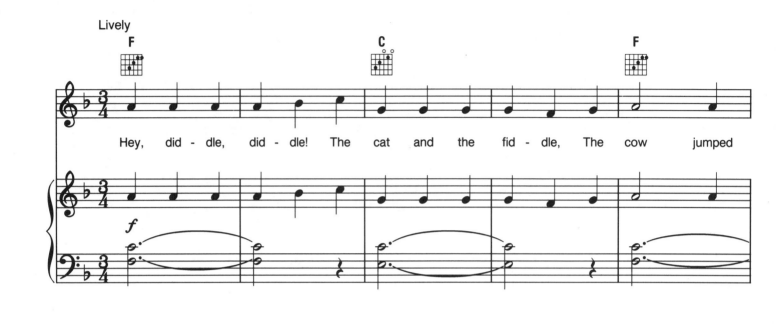

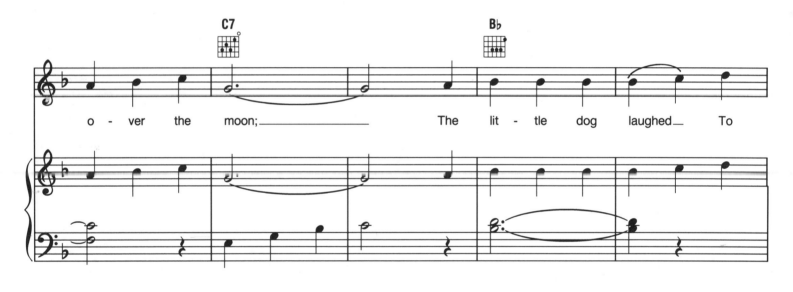

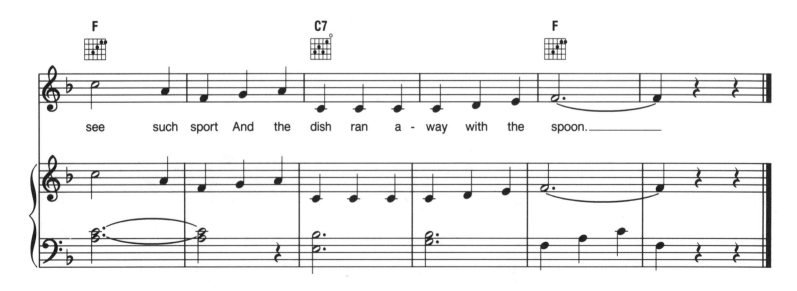

Copyright © 1988 by HAL LEONARD PUBLISHING CORPORATION
International Copyright Secured   ALL RIGHTS RESERVED   Printed in the U.S.A.

HICKORY DICKORY DOCK

Copyright © 1988 by HAL LEONARD PUBLISHING CORPORATION
International Copyright Secured   ALL RIGHTS RESERVED   Printed in the U.S.A.

HOME ON THE RANGE

Traditional

Copyright © 1995 by HAL LEONARD CORPORATION
International Copyright Secured   All Rights Reserved

Additional Lyrics

3. Where the air is so pure and the zephyrs so free,
   And the breezes so balmy and light;
   Oh, I would not exchange my home on the range
   For the glittering cities so bright.
   To Chorus

4. Oh, give me a land where the bright diamond sand
   Flows leisurely down with the stream,
   Where the graceful white swan glides slowly along,
   Like a maid in a heavenly dream.
   To Chorus

HOT CROSS BUNS

Traditional

Moderately

Hot cross buns! Hot cross buns! One a pen-ny, two a pen-ny, hot cross buns! If you have no daugh-ters, if you have no daugh-ters, if you have no daugh-ters, then give them to your sons. But if you have none of these lit-tle elves, then you must eat them all your-selves!

Copyright © 2000 by HAL LEONARD CORPORATION
International Copyright Secured   All Rights Reserved

HUMPTY DUMPTY

Hump - ty Dump - ty sat on a wall, Hump - ty

Dump - ty had a great fall; All the King's hors - es and

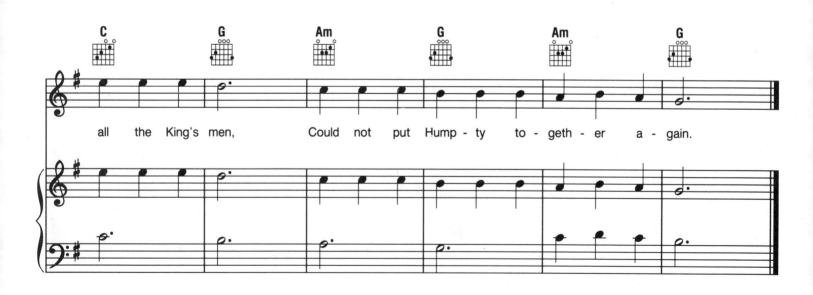

all the King's men, Could not put Hump - ty to - geth - er a - gain.

Copyright © 1988 by HAL LEONARD PUBLISHING CORPORATION
International Copyright Secured   ALL RIGHTS RESERVED   Printed in the U.S.A.

HUSH, LITTLE BABY

Carolina Folk Lullaby

Copyright © 2000 by HAL LEONARD CORPORATION
International Copyright Secured   All Rights Reserved

I WHISTLE A HAPPY TUNE

from THE KING AND I

Words by OSCAR HAMMERSTEIN II
Music by RICHARD RODGERS

Copyright © 1951 by Richard Rodgers and Oscar Hammerstein II.   Copyright Renewed
Williamson Music Co., owner of publication and allied rights for all countries of the Western Hemisphere and Japan.
All Rights Administered by Chappell & Co., Inc.
International Copyright Secured   ALL RIGHTS RESERVED   Printed in the U.S.A.
Unauthorized copying, arranging, adapting, recording or public performance is an infringement of copyright.
Infringers are liable under the law.

IT'S A SMALL WORLD

from Disneyland and Walt Disney World's IT'S A SMALL WORLD

Words and Music by RICHARD M. SHERMAN
and ROBERT B. SHERMAN

March Tempo

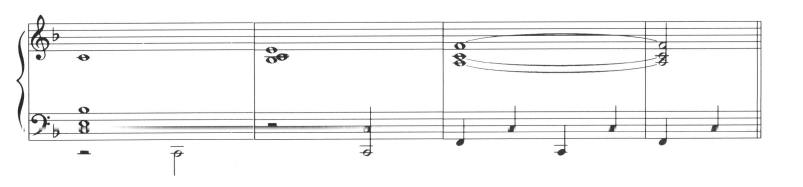

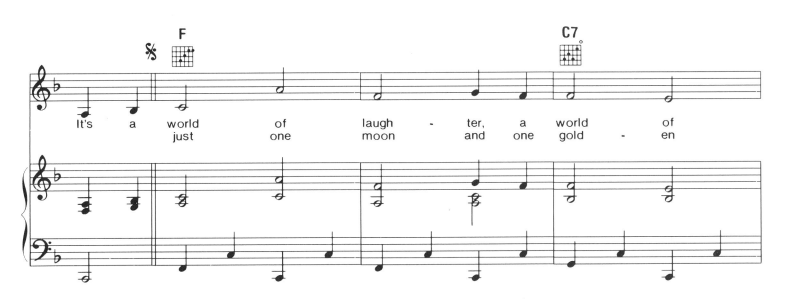

It's a world of laugh - ter, a world of
just one moon and one gold - en

© 1963 Wonderland Music Company, Inc.
Copyright Renewed
All Rights Reserved   Used by Permission

114

I'M LATE
from Walt Disney's ALICE IN WONDERLAND

Words by Bob Hilliard
Music by Sammy Fain

I'm late, I'm late for a ver-y im-por-tant date. No

time to say hel-lo, good-bye, I'm late, I'm late, I'm late, I'm late and

when I wave, I lose the time I save. My fuz-zy ears and

© 1949 Walt Disney Music Company
Copyright Renewed
All Rights Reserved   Used by Permission

I'M POPEYE THE SAILOR MAN

Theme from the Paramount Cartoon POPEYE THE SAILOR
Theme from the Paramount Motion Picture POPEYE

Words and Music by
SAMMY LERNER

Copyright © 1934 (Renewed 1961) by Famous Music Corporation
International Copyright Secured   All Rights Reserved

KUM BA YAH

Traditional Spiritual

Copyright © 2000 by HAL LEONARD CORPORATION
International Copyright Secured   All Rights Reserved

IF YOU'RE HAPPY AND YOU KNOW IT

Words and Music by
L. SMITH

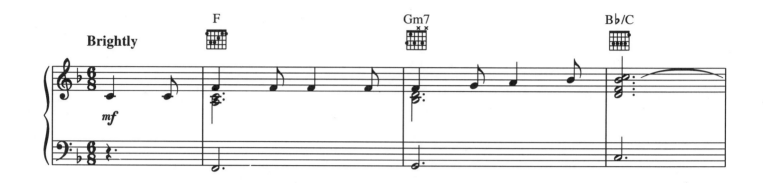

If you're hap - py and you know it, clap your
hap - py and you know it, tap your
hap - py and you know it, nod your

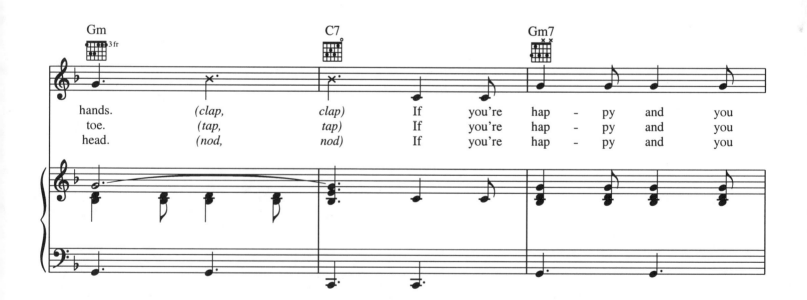

hands.   (clap,   clap)   If you're hap - py and you
toe.   (tap,   tap)   If you're hap - py and you
head.   (nod,   nod)   If you're hap - py and you

Copyright © 2000 by HAL LEONARD CORPORATION
International Copyright Secured   All Rights Reserved

IT'S RAINING, IT'S POURING

Traditional

Copyright © 1995 by HAL LEONARD CORPORATION
International Copyright Secured   All Rights Reserved

LAVENDER BLUE
(Dilly Dilly)
from Walt Disney's SO DEAR TO MY HEART

Words by LARRY MOREY
Music by ELIOT DANIEL

© 1948 Walt Disney Music Company
Copyright Renewed
International Copyright Secured   All Rights Reserved

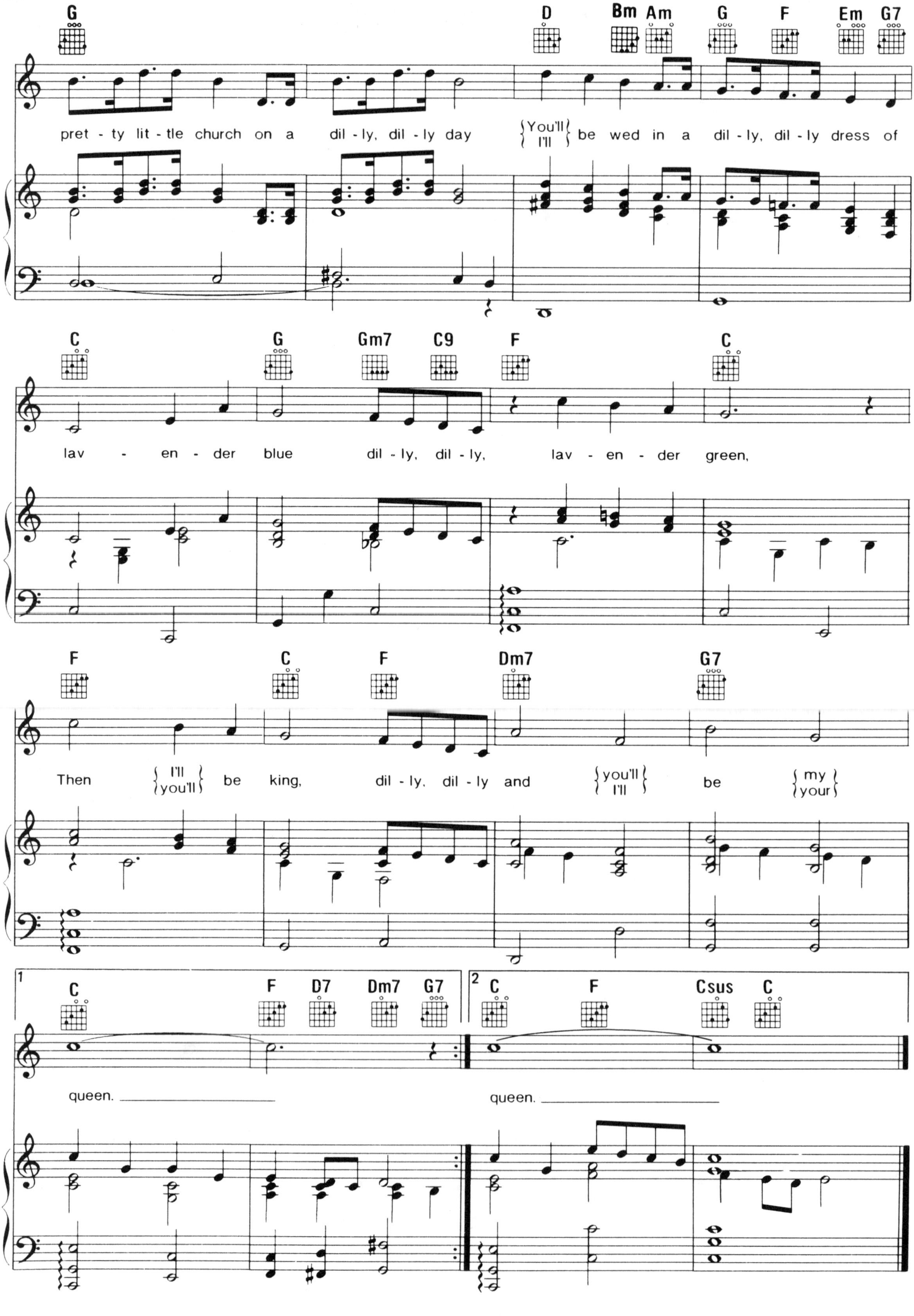

G D Bm Am G F Em G7
pret - ty lit - tle church on a dil - ly, dil - ly day {You'll / I'll} be wed in a dil - ly, dil - ly dress of
C G Gm7 C9 F C
lav - en - der blue dil - ly, dil - ly, lav - en - der green,
F C F Dm7 G7
Then {I'll / you'll} be king, dil - ly, dil - ly and {you'll / I'll} be {my / your}
1 C F D7 Dm7 G7
queen.
2 C F Csus C
queen.

LITTLE BO-PEEP

Copyright © 1988 by HAL LEONARD PUBLISHING CORPORATION
International Copyright Secured   ALL RIGHTS RESERVED   Printed in the U.S.A.

LITTLE APRIL SHOWER
from Walt Disney's BAMBI

Words by LARRY MOREY
Music by FRANK CHURCHILL

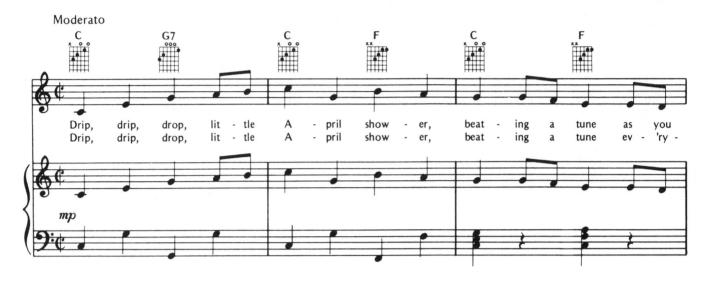

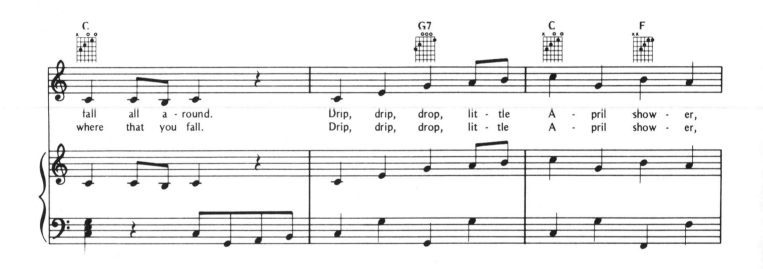

© 1942 Wonderland Music Company, Inc.
Copyright Renewed
All Rights Reserved   Used by Permission

LITTLE BOY BLUE

Copyright © 1988 by HAL LEONARD PUBLISHING CORPORATION
International Copyright Secured   ALL RIGHTS RESERVED   Printed in the U.S.A.

LONDON BRIDGE

3. Iron bars will bend and break,
   Bend and break, bend and break;
   Iron bars will bend and break,
   My fair lady.

4. Build it up with gold and silver,
   Gold and silver, gold and silver;
   Build it up with gold and silver,
   My fair lady.

Copyright © 1988 by HAL LEONARD PUBLISHING CORPORATION
International Copyright Secured   ALL RIGHTS RESERVED   Printed in the U.S.A.

MAH-NÁ MAH-NÁ

By PIERO UMILIANI

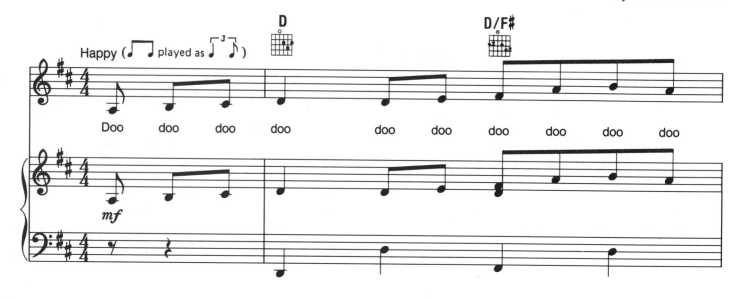

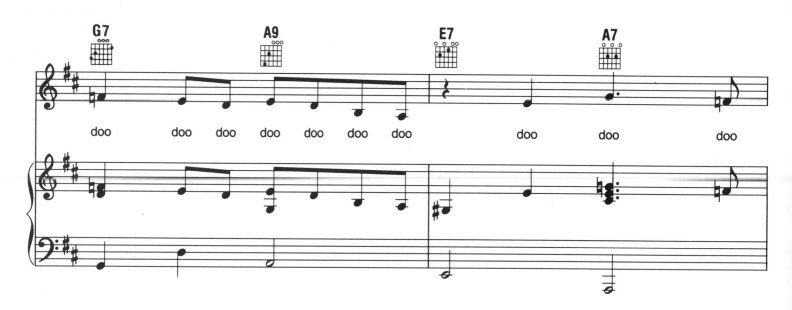

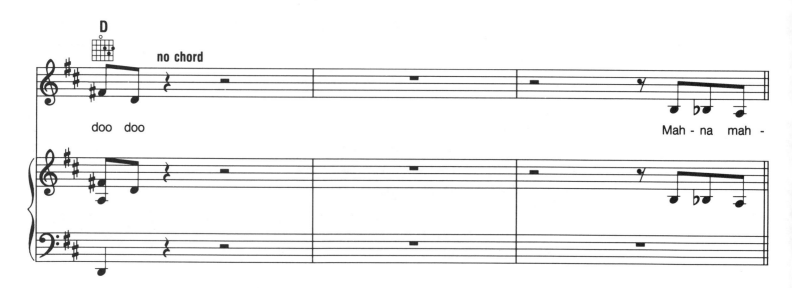

Copyright © 1966 by Edward B. Marks Music Company for the world except Italy
Copyright Renewed
International Copyright Secured   All Rights Reserved
Used by Permission

THE MAN ON THE FLYING TRAPEZE

Words by GEORGE LEYBOURNE
Music by ALFRED LEE

Copyright © 2000 by HAL LEONARD CORPORATION
International Copyright Secured   All Rights Reserved

140

Additional Lyrics

4. One night as usual I want to her dear home,
   And found there her mother and father alone.
   I asked for my love, and soon 'twas made known,
   To my horror, that she'd run away.
   She packed up her boxes and eloped in the night
   With him, with the greatest of ease.
   From two stories high he had lowered her down
   To the ground on his flying trapeze.

   Chorus

5. Some months after that I went into a hall;
   To my surprise I found there on the wall
   A bill in red letters which did my heart gall,
   That she was appearing with him,
   He'd taught her gymnastics and dressed her in tights
   To help him live at ease.
   He'd made her assume a masculine name,
   And now she goes on the trapeze.

   Chorus

MICHAEL ROW THE BOAT ASHORE

Traditional Folksong

Copyright © 2000 by HAL LEONARD CORPORATION
International Copyright Secured   All Rights Reserved

MICKEY MOUSE MARCH

Words and Music by
JIMMIE DODD

© 1955 WALT DISNEY MUSIC COMPANY
Copyright Renewed
International Copyright Secured   Made in U.S.A.   All Rights Reserved

146

Additional Interludes

5. We have fun and we play safely!
6. Look both ways when you cross crossings!
7. Don't take chances! Play with safety!
8. When you ride your bike be careful!
9. Play a little, work a little.

10. Sing a song while you are working!
11. It will make your burden lighter.
12. Do a good turn for your neighbor.
13. You can learn things while you're playing.
14. It's a lot of fun to learn things.

ROCK-A-BYE, BABY

Dreamily

Traditional

Copyright © 2000 by HAL LEONARD CORPORATION
International Copyright Secured   All Rights Reserved

OLD MACDONALD HAD A FARM

Traditional Children's Song

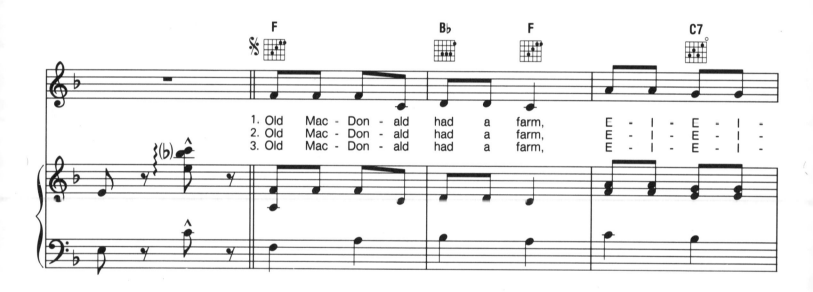

1. Old Mac-Don-ald had a farm, E - I - E - I -
2. Old Mac-Don-ald had a farm, E - I - E - I -
3. Old Mac-Don-ald had a farm, E - I - E - I -

O,_____ And on his farm he had a cow, E - I - E - I -
O,_____ And on his farm he had a pig, E - I - E - I -
O,_____ And on his farm he had a duck, E - I - E - I -

Copyright © 2000 by HAL LEONARD CORPORATION
International Copyright Secured   All Rights Reserved

4. Old MacDonald had a farm,
E-I-E-I-O,
And on his farm he had a horse,
E-I-E-I-O,
With a neigh-neigh here and a neigh-neigh there, *etc.*

5. Old MacDonald had a farm,
E-I-E-I-O,
And on his farm he had a donkey,
E-I-E-I-O,
With a hee-haw here, *etc.*

6. Old MacDonald had a farm,
E-I-E-I-O,
And on his farm he had some chickens,
E-I-E-I-O,
With a chick-chick here, *etc.*

For additional verses, add your own animals.

ON TOP OF OLD SMOKY

Moderately waltz

On top of old Smok -

y, _____ All cov - er'd with snow, _____

_____ I lost my true lov - er, _____ For

Copyright © 1988 by HAL LEONARD PUBLISHING CORPORATION
International Copyright Secured   ALL RIGHTS RESERVED   Printed in the U.S.A.

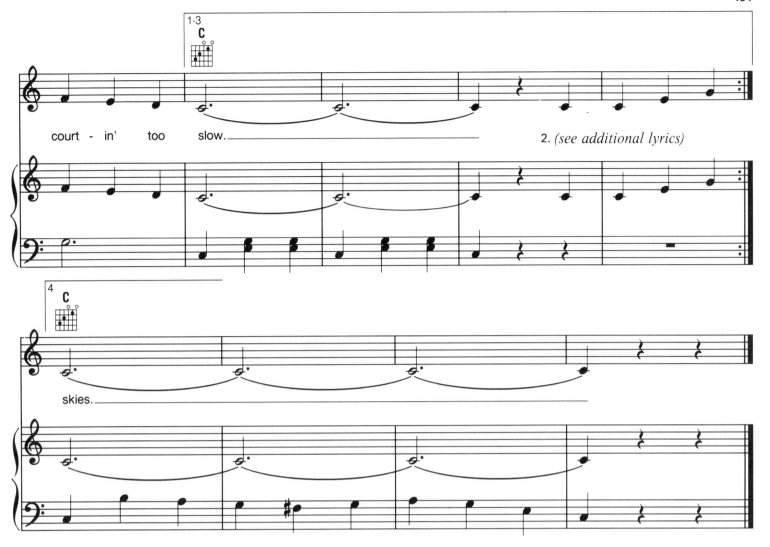

2. *(see additional lyrics)*

2. A-courtin's a pleasure,
   A-flirtin's a grief,
   A false-hearted lover -
   Is worse than a thief.

3. For a thief, he will rob you,
   And take what you have,
   But a false-hearted lover -
   Sends you to your grave.

4. She'll hug you and kiss you,
   And tell you more lies,
   Than the ties on the railroad,
   Or the stars in the skies.

PART OF YOUR WORLD

from Walt Disney's THE LITTLE MERMAID

Lyrics by HOWARD ASHMAN
Music by ALAN MENKEN

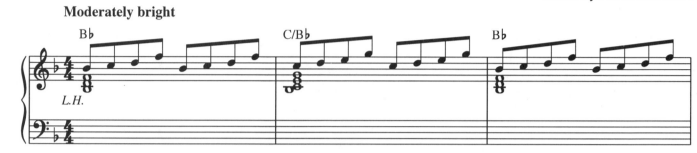

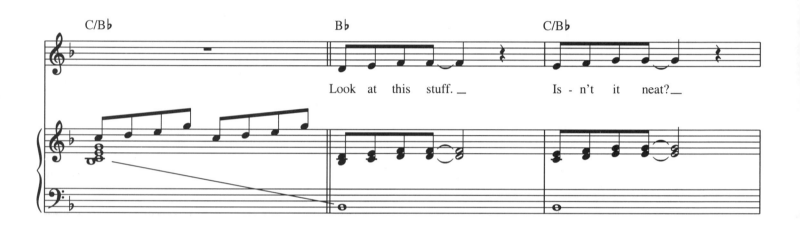

Look at this stuff. _ Is - n't it neat? _

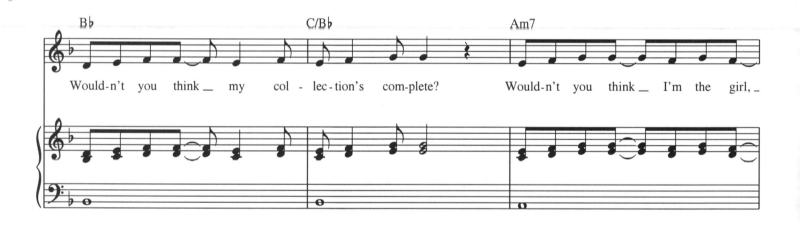

Would-n't you think _ my col - lec-tion's com-plete? Would-n't you think _ I'm the girl, _

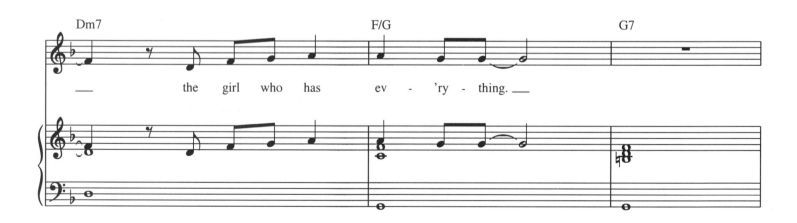

_ the girl who has ev - 'ry - thing. _

© 1988 Walt Disney Music Company and Wonderland Music Company, Inc.
International Copyright Secured   All Rights Reserved

Look at this trove, _ treas - ures un - told. _ How man - y won - ders can

one ca - vern hold? Look - ing a - round _ here you'd think, _ sure, she's got

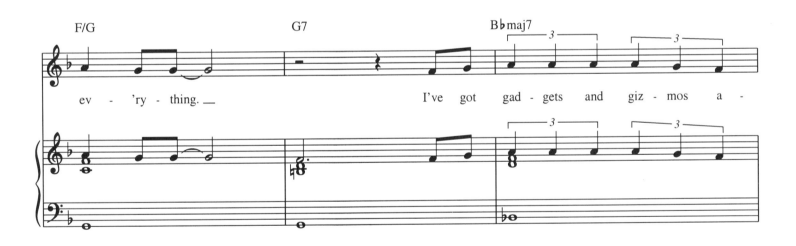

ev - 'ry - thing. _ I've got gad - gets and giz - mos a -

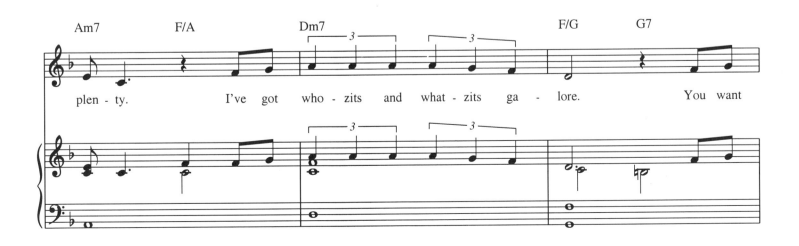

plen - ty. I've got who - zits and what - zits ga - lore. You want

154

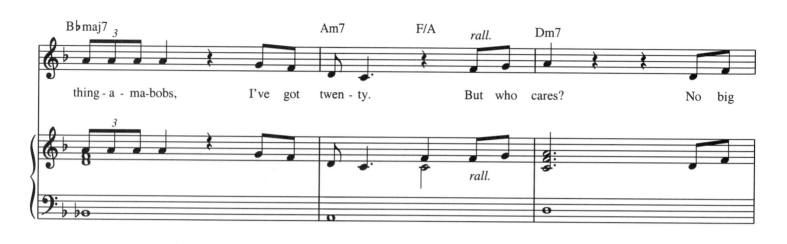

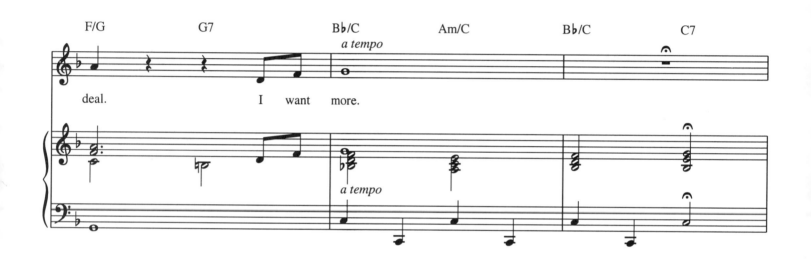

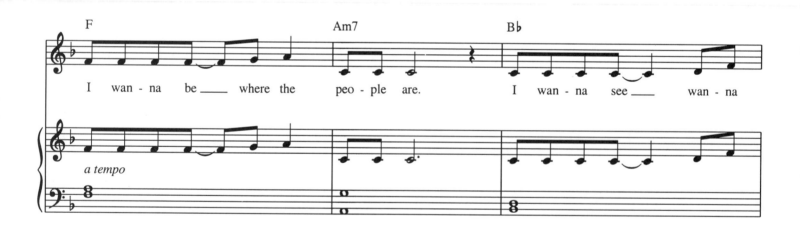

POLLY WOLLY DOODLE

Bright, with humor

1. Oh, I

went down South for to see my Sal, Sing-ing pol-ly-wol-ly-doo-dle all the
2. Sal she is a__ maid-en fair, Sing-ing pol-ly-wol-ly-doo-dle all the
3. grass-hop-per sit-tin' on a rail-road track, Sing-ing pol-ly-wol-ly-doo-dle all the

day. My__ Sal she is a spunk-y gal, Sing-ing
day. With__ curl-y eyes and laugh-ing hair, Sing-ing
day. A - pick-in' his teeth with a car-pet tack, Sing-ing

Copyright © 1988 by HAL LEONARD PUBLISHING CORPORATION
International Copyright Secured   ALL RIGHTS RESERVED   Printed in the U.S.A.

4. Oh, I went to bed, but it wasn't no use,
   Singing polly-wolly-doodle all the day.
   My feet stuck out like a chicken roost,
   Singing polly-wolly-doodle all the day.
   Chorus

5. Behind the barn down on my knees,
   Singing polly-wolly-doodle all the day.
   I thought I heard a chicken sneeze,
   Singing polly-wolly-doodle all the day.
   Chorus

6. He sneezed so hard with the whooping cough,
   Singing polly-wolly-doodle all the day.
   He sneezed his head and tail right off,
   Singing polly-wolly-doodle all the day.
   Chorus

ROW, ROW, ROW YOUR BOAT

Traditional

Copyright © 2000 by HAL LEONARD CORPORATION
International Copyright Secured   All Rights Reserved

Mer - ri - ly, mer - ri - ly, mer - ri - ly, mer - ri - ly, Life is but a dream.

A SUGGESTED ACTIVITY

"Row, Row, Row Your Boat" is a famous "round" that has been sung and enjoyed by people of all ages. When sung correctly, the melody actually goes around and around. Here's how it works: The singers are divided into two groups. The first group sings the first line alone. At this point, the second group starts at the beginning, while the first group continues with the second line. In this manner, the groups are always exactly one line apart as the tune is repeated. The last time through, the second group sings the final line alone just as the first group sang the opening line alone. Try it . . . it's fun!

SESAME STREET THEME

Words by BRUCE HART,
JON STONE and JOE RAPOSO
Music by JOE RAPOSO

Copyright © 1970 Sesame Street Music, Inc.
Copyright Renewed
All Rights Administered by Sony ATV Music Publishing, 8 Music Square West, Nashville, TN 37203
International Copyright Secured   All Rights Reserved

A SPOONFUL OF SUGAR
from Walt Disney's MARY POPPINS

Words and Music by RICHARD M. SHERMAN
and ROBERT B. SHERMAN

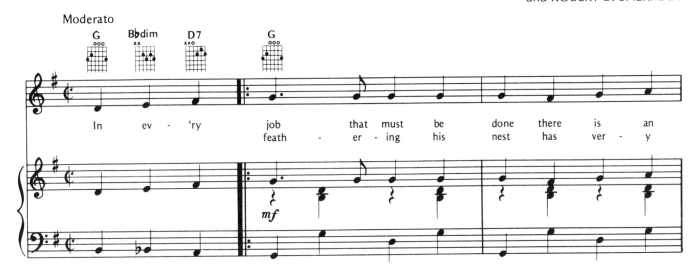

© 1963 Wonderland Music Company, Inc.
Copyright Renewed
International Copyright Secured   All Rights Reserved

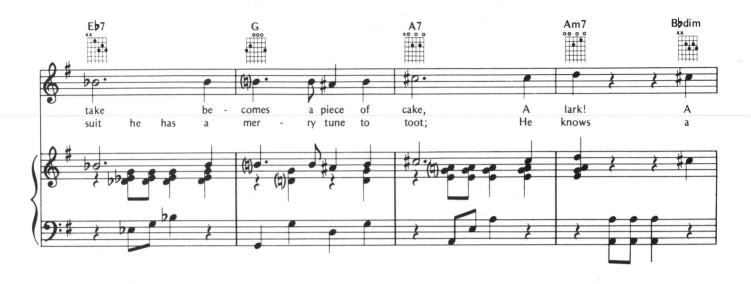

take be - comes a piece of cake, A lark! A
suit he has a mer - ry tune to toot; He knows a

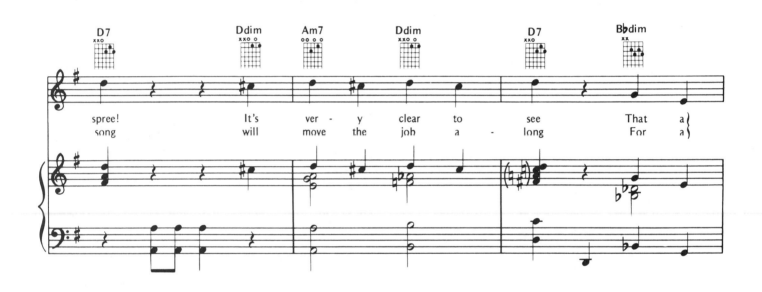

spree! It's ver - y clear to see That a
song will move the job a - long For a

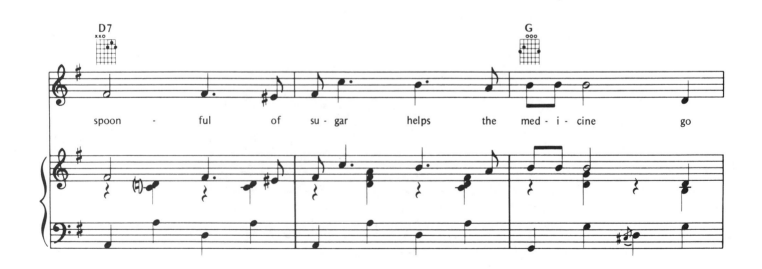

spoon - ful of su - gar helps the med - i - cine go

SHE'LL BE COMIN' 'ROUND THE MOUNTAIN

Copyright © 1988 by HAL LEONARD PUBLISHING CORPORATION
International Copyright Secured   ALL RIGHTS RESERVED   Printed in the U.S.A.

3. Oh, we'll all go to meet her when she comes,
   Oh, we'll all go to meet her when she comes,
   Oh, we'll all go to meet her,
   Oh, we'll all go to meet her,
   Oh, we'll all go to meet her when she comes.

4. We'll be singin' ''Hallelujah'' when she comes,
   We'll be singin' ''Hallelujah'' when she comes,
   We'll be singin' ''Hallelujah,''
   We'll be singin' ''Hallelujah,''
   We'll be singin' ''Hallelujah'' when she comes.

THE SIAMESE CAT SONG
from Walt Disney's LADY AND THE TRAMP

Words and Music by PEGGY LEE
and SONNY BURKE

© 1953 Walt Disney Music Company
Copyright Renewed
All Rights Reserved   Used by Permission

We are Si - am - ese with ver - y

dain - ty claws.   Please ob - serv - ing paws con - tain - ing   dain - ty claws.

Now we look - in' o - ver our new dom - i - cile.   If we like we stay for may - be

quite a - while.

SKIP TO MY LOU

Traditional

Copyright © 2000 by HAL LEONARD CORPORATION
International Copyright Secured   All Rights Reserved

2. I'll find another one, prettier than you,
   I'll find another one, prettier than you,
   I'll find another one, prettier than you,
   Skip to my Lou, my darling.

3. Little red wagon, painted blue.

4. Can't get a red bird, a blue bird'll do.

5. Cows in the meadow, moo, moo, moo.

6. Flies in the buttermilk, shoo, shoo, shoo.

SUPERCALIFRAGILISTICEXPIALIDOCIOUS

from Walt Disney's MARY POPPINS

Words and Music by RICHARD M. SHERMAN
and ROBERT B. SHERMAN

© 1963 Wonderland Music Company, Inc.
Copyright Renewed
All Rights Reserved   Used by Permission

TEN LITTLE INDIANS

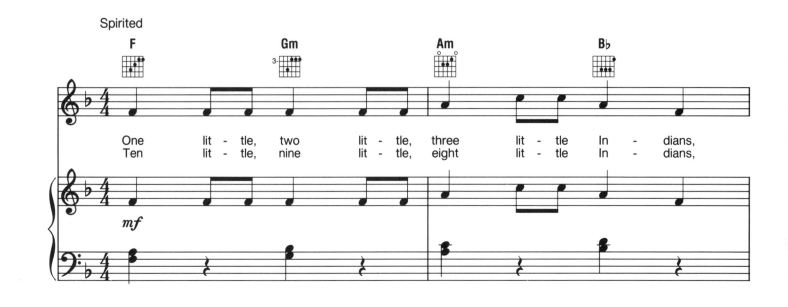

One lit-tle, two lit-tle, three lit-tle In-dians,
Ten lit-tle, nine lit-tle, eight lit-tle In-dians,

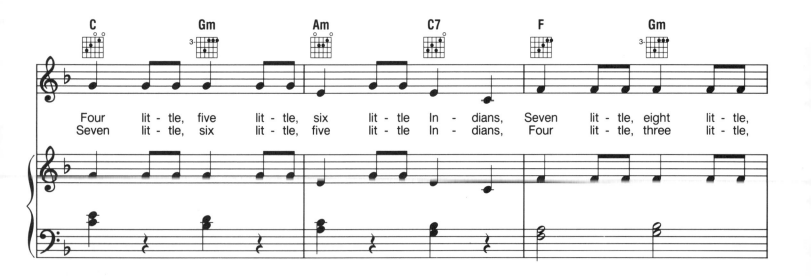

Four lit-tle, five lit-tle, six lit-tle In-dians, Seven lit-tle, eight lit-tle,
Seven lit-tle, six lit-tle, five lit-tle In-dians, Four lit-tle, three lit-tle,

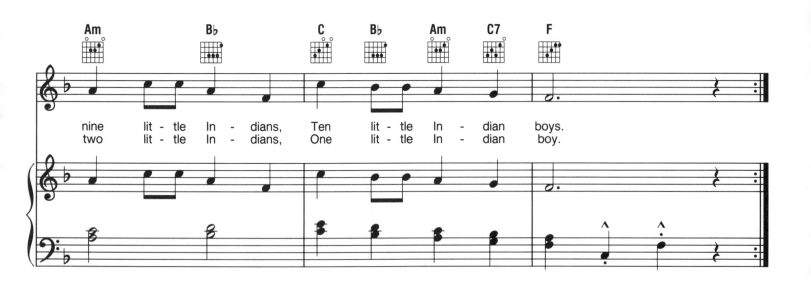

nine lit-tle In-dians, Ten lit-tle In-dian boys.
two lit-tle In-dians, One lit-tle In-dian boy.

Copyright © 1988 by HAL LEONARD PUBLISHING CORPORATION
International Copyright Secured   ALL RIGHTS RESERVED   Printed in the U.S.A.

THERE'S A HOLE IN THE BUCKET

Traditional

Additional Lyrics

3. With what shall I fix it, dear Liza, etc.
4. With a straw, dear Henry, etc.
5. But the straw is too long, dear Liza, etc.
6. Then cut it, dear Henry, etc.
7. With what shall I cut it, dear Liza, etc.
8. With a knife, dear Henry, etc.
9. But the knife is too dull, dear Liza, etc.
10. Then sharpen it, dear Liza, etc.

11. With what shall I sharpen it, dear Liza, etc.
12. With a stone, dear Henry, etc.
13. But the stone is too dry, dear Liza, etc.
14. Then wet it, dear Henry, etc.
15. With what shall I wet it, dear Liza, etc.
16. With water, dear Henry, etc.
17. In what shall I carry it, dear Liza, etc.
18. In a bucket, dear Henry, etc.

19. There's a hole in the bucket, dear Liza, etc.

Copyright © 1994 by HAL LEONARD CORPORATION
International Copyright Secured   All Rights Reserved

THIS OLD MAN

*Two . . . . on the shoe
*Three . . . on the tree
*Four . . . . on the door
*Five . . . . on the hive
*Six . . . . . on the sticks
*Seven . . . up in heaven
*Eight . . . on the gate
*Nine . . . . on the line
*Ten . . . . . once again

Copyright © 1988 by HAL LEONARD PUBLISHING CORPORATION
International Copyright Secured   ALL RIGHTS RESERVED   Printed in the U.S.A.

THREE BLIND MICE

Copyright © 1988 by HAL LEONARD PUBLISHING CORPORATION
International Copyright Secured   ALL RIGHTS RESERVED   Printed in the U.S.A.

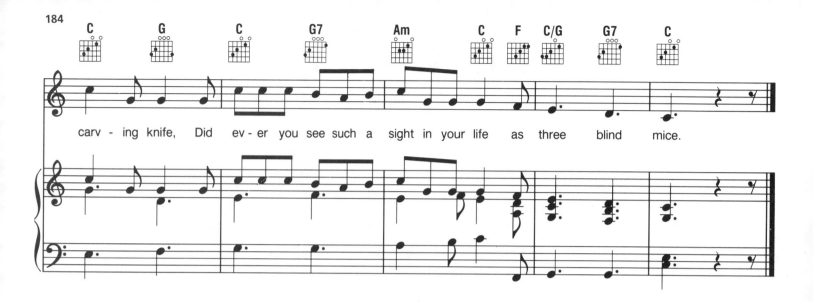

carv - ing knife, Did ev - er you see such a sight in your life as three blind mice.

YANKEE DOODLE

With spirit

1. Yan - kee Doo - dle went to town A - rid - ing on a
2. Fath'r and I went down to camp A - long with Cap - tain
3. There was Cap - tain Wash - ing - ton Up - on a slap - ping

po - ny,   Stuck a feath - er in his cap And
Good - win.   There we saw the men and boys As
stal - lion,   Giv - ing or - ders to his men; I

Copyright © 1988 by HAL LEONARD PUBLISHING CORPORATION
International Copyright Secured   ALL RIGHTS RESERVED   Printed in the U.S.A.

THIS TRAIN

Traditional

With spirit

1. This train is bound for glo - ry, this train. ____

2.-6. *See additional lyrics*

This train is bound for glo - ry,

this train. ____ This train is

Copyright © 1995 by HAL LEONARD CORPORATION
International Copyright Secured   All Rights Reserved

187

Additional Lyrics

2. **This train don't carry no gamblers,** (*3 times*)
   No hypocrites, no midnight ramblers,
   This train is bound for glory, this train.

3. **This train don't carry no liars,** (*3 times*)
   No hypocrites and no high flyers,
   This train is bound for glory, this train.

4. **This train is built for speed now,** (*3 times*)
   Fastest train you ever did see,
   This train is bound for glory, this train.

5. **This train you don't pay no transportation,** (*3 times*)
   No Jim Crow and no discrimination,
   This train is bound for glory, this train.

6. **This train don't carry no rustlers,** (*3 times*)
   Sidestreet walkers, two-bit hustlers,
   This train is bound for glory, this train.

TWINKLE, TWINKLE LITTLE STAR

Traditional

Copyright © 2000 by HAL LEONARD CORPORATION
International Copyright Secured   All Rights Reserved

Parody

Starkle, starkle, little twink,
How I wonder what you think!
Up above the world so high,
Think you own the whole darn sky?
Starkle, starkle, little twink,
You're not so great,
That's what I think!

UNDER THE SEA
from Walt Disney's THE LITTLE MERMAID

Lyrics by HOWARD ASHMAN
Music by ALAN MENKEN

© 1988 Walt Disney Music Company and Wonderland Music Company, Inc.
International Copyright Secured   All Rights Reserved

191

197

THE UNBIRTHDAY SONG
from Walt Disney's ALICE IN WONDERLAND

Words and Music by MACK DAVID,
AL HOFFMAN and JERRY LIVINGSTON

© 1948 Walt Disney Music Company
Copyright Renewed
International Copyright Secured   All Rights Reserved

202

Patter

A WHOLE NEW WORLD

from Walt Disney's ALADDIN

Music by ALAN MENKEN
Lyrics by TIM RICE

© 1992 Wonderland Music Company, Inc. and Walt Disney Music Company
All Rights Reserved   Used by Permission

WHEN I'M SIXTY-FOUR

from YELLOW SUBMARINE

Words and Music by JOHN LENNON
and PAUL McCARTNEY

Moderately

When I get old - er, los - ing my hair__ man - y years from now__

Will you still be send - ing me a val - en - tine,__

Copyright © 1967 Sony/ATV Songs LLC
Copyright Renewed
All Rights Administered by Sony/ATV Music Publishing, 8 Music Square West, Nashville, TN 37203
International Copyright Secured   All Rights Reserved

WHEN JOHNNY COMES MARCHING HOME

Words and Music by
PATRICK SARSFIELD GILMORE (LOUIS LAMBERT)

Copyright © 1995 by HAL LEONARD CORPORATION
International Copyright Secured   All Rights Reserved

WHEN THE SAINTS GO MARCHING IN

Words by KATHERINE E. PURVIS
Music by JAMES M. BLACK

Copyright © 2000 by HAL LEONARD CORPORATION
International Copyright Secured   All Rights Reserved

THE WONDERFUL THING ABOUT TIGGERS

from Walt Disney's THE MANY ADVENTURES OF WINNIE THE POOH

Words and Music by RICHARD M. SHERMAN
and ROBERT B. SHERMAN

Very brightly

1. The (3.) won-der-ful thing a-bout tig-gers ___ is tig-gers are won-der-ful
2. won-der-ful thing a-bout tig-gers ___ is tig-gers are won-der-ful

things! Their tops are made out of rub-ber; ___ their bot-toms are made out of
chaps! They're load-ed with vim and with vig-or; ___ they love to leap in your

springs! They're bounc-y, trounc-y, flounc-y, pounc-y,
laps! They're jump-y, bump-y, clump-y, thump-y,
Fun! Fun! Fun! Fun!

© 1964 Wonderland Music Company, Inc.
Copyright Renewed
All Rights Reserved   Used by Permission

YELLOW SUBMARINE

Words and Music by
JOHN LENNON and PAUL McCARTNEY

March tempo

In the town _____ where I was born lived a man _____ who sailed to sea. And he told _____ us of his life _____ in the land _____ of sub-ma-rines. So we

Copyright © 1966 NORTHERN SONGS LIMITED
All Rights Controlled and Administered by SBK BLACKWOOD MUSIC INC. under license from ATV MUSIC (MACLEN)
All Rights Reserved   International Copyright Secured

Chorus:

We all live in a yel - low sub - ma - rine,

yel - low sub - ma - rine, yel - low sub - ma - rine. We all live in a

yel - low sub - ma - rine, yel - low sub - ma - rine,

yel - low sub - ma - rine. {And our friends _____ are all on
As we live _____ a life of

YOU'VE GOT A FRIEND IN ME

from Walt Disney's TOY STORY
from Walt Disney Pictures' TOY STORY 2 - A Pixar Film

Music and Lyrics by
RANDY NEWMAN

© 1995 Walt Disney Music Company
All Rights Reserved   Used by Permission

ZIP-A-DEE-DOO-DAH
from Walt Disney's SONG OF THE SOUTH

Words by RAY GILBERT
Music by ALLIE WRUBEL

© 1945 Walt Disney Music Company
Copyright Renewed
International Copyright Secured All Rights Reserved

WINNIE THE POOH

from Walt Disney's THE MANY ADVENTURES OF WINNIE THE POOH

Words and Music by RICHARD M. SHERMAN
and ROBERT B. SHERMAN

© 1963 Wonderland Music Company, Inc.
Copyright Renewed
All Rights Reserved   Used by Permission

Tempo I

A don-key named Ee - yore is his friend, and
Kan - ga and lit - tle Roo. _____ There's Rab - bit and Pig - let
and there's Owl but most of all Win - nie the Pooh.

D.S. al Coda

CODA

Wil - ly nil - ly sil - ly ole bear.

no chord